Amazing Stories in Rhyme

by

Jock Sprockett

with illustrations by Stewart M Dearden

First edition published in Great Britain in 2006
by BookForce UK

A Four O'Clock Press title.

ISBN 13 9781-905108-41-1

The policy of BookForce UK is to use papers that are natural, renewable and recyclable products made from wood grown in sustainable forests wherever possible.

BookForce UK Ltd.
50 Albemarle Street
London W1S 4BD
www.bookforce.co.uk

Hello, my name is Jock Sprockett.
I am 8 years old and live in the lovely Scottish Borders.
I travel all over the world collecting the most
amazing stories for Children.
Here is my latest collection of stories,
I really hope you enjoy them...

-

If you would like to find out more about me
and my stories please visit my website

www.jocksprockett.co.uk

by

Jock Sprockett

with illustrations by

Stewart M Dearden

CONTENTS

BARNYBUS THE WHALE

Now listen closely to this tale
Of Barnybus the joker whale,
Who loved to wear those fake shark's fins
To scare small fish out of their skins!

All creatures living in the deep
Felt *terrorized.* He thought it neat
To tie up Ollie Octopus.
He laughed and laughed, did Barnybus.

With pliers poised he'd take a run
And pinch Joe Haddock on the bum!
He felt no sorrow, felt no shame,
When Larry Lobster got the blame.

One day with HUGE elastic band
He pinged Sam Cod upon dry land.
"I'll get you back for this!" roared Sam.
The whale stuck out his tongue — and scrammed!

But late that night on ocean blue,
A whaling ship came into view!
That big whale blubbered for his Mum,
When he saw the whaler's — HARPOON GUN.

He pleaded "MERCY! SPARE MY LIFE!"
And promised *never* to cause strife.
For all the creatures in the sea
He offered to bake scones for tea.

"Too late for that!" the Whaler said
And aimed the gun at Barny's head.
"Now say your prayers, Mister Whale!"
Poor Barnybus had turned quite pale.

Then suddenly, to great surprise,
The Whaler pulled off his disguise
Revealing how that crafty bod
Had all the time been — Sam the Cod!

And laughing loudly at the sight
Of Barny's sad pathetic plight,
Sam Cod said, "Please take my advice.
In future, Barnybus — *be nice.*"

Ten thousand fishes in the sea
Swished, and danced around with glee,
Until at last the porpoise spoke:
"Now that was one WHALE — of a joke!"

ROOSTER PIE

Kirsty, from the Isle of Skye,
Prepared for supper Rooster Pie.
She stirred some flour with eggs and milk,
Produced a pastry smooth as silk.
Plucked a rooster, stuffed him in,
Ready — steady — cook — begin!

Just then, that rooster cocked an eye:
"Ha Ha!" he crowed, "I didn't die!
I just *pretended* to be dead.
I'm outa' here RIGHT NOW!" he said.

Huge wings of skin began to flap,
(The draught blew Kirsty on her back)
As bird, attached to baking bowl,
Took off. The girl cried, "SAVE MY SOUL!"
And as she watched them soar up high
She screamed, "I've baked a flying pie!"

As bony wings flashed quick as lightning.
The object's speed was simply frightening.
They whipped pie far across the ocean,
Where Rooster caused a great commotion!

The pie arrived without delay
In New York City, U.S.A.
A baseball player spied him first
(Of course, the poor guy feared the worst)
So loudly did he scream and shout:
"Here comes a U.F.O. — QUICK! LOOK OUT!"

Before you could say, 'Al Capone'
The President was on the phone.
He roared, "Aliens — in my backyard?
No way! — call out the National Guard!"

The Army and the best Marines
Were sent to blow to smithereens,
This alien crew from outer space
And wipe that smile from Rooster's face.
Soon bullets whizzed and missiles flared,
But Rooster Pie was far from scared.

He fought right back with chunks of pastry
Which all the soldiers found so tasty,
They stopped bombarding Rooster Pie,
Then had a picnic (on the sly.)

The Pie flew south towards Brazil,
And kept on going further still.
On and on, and on, he flew
Across Brazil, above Peru.
The strangest things Pie ever saw
Took place down in Bolivia.

The Rooster viewed such wondrous scenes
From Paraguay to Argentine.
But hungry now, and quite forlorn,
He landed in a field of corn.

And it was there he met Miss Jen,
A dark and sultry, *gorgeous* hen.
It must have been love at first sight,
For Rooster Pie, proposed that night!
"Ooh yes!" swooned Jen, "I'll marry you!"
Cried Rooster, "COCK — A — DOODLE — DO!"

That pair lived happy ever after,
But now this tale gets slightly dafter.
As wedding plans were made so hasty,
Instead of cake, the guests ate PASTRY!

HECTOR THE HAGGIS

Hector the hairy-nosed haggis
Always did what young haggis do best,
He ran round and round on a hillside
Without ever taking a rest.

With long legs attached to his left side,
Much shorter ones under his right,
He could not run straight if he wanted,
So he circled by day and by night.

Apart from some stones and rough heather,
There's not much on a hillside to see,
So the life of a hairy-nosed haggis
Is boring as boring can be.

Young Hector just *longed* for adventure,
So one day he concocted a plan
To start a new life in the City,
Then, to Glasgow, in circles, he ran!

All alone in the City of Glasgow,
Although searching until he was grey,
Hector could not find work for a haggis
Who just ran round in circles all day.

Then one morning Slick Jimmy, a street cat,
With incredible luck he did meet.
Said Jimmy, "A travelling fairground's
Just arrived in the park near my street."

Just as fast as those queer legs could take him,
In circles bold Hector he *flew*
To ask if the man from the fairground
Had work that a haggis could do.

"Good morning, my name it is Hector."
He presented himself to the boss.
"Have you jobs for a hairy-nosed haggis?"
The man seemed at first, at a loss.

After scratching his head for a moment,
Said, "I've had an *incredible* thought!
I just can't find the right type of engine
For that new carousel which I've bought.

Do you think you could pull loads of children,
Round and round by yourself all day long?"
Hector cried, "What a *brilliant* idea!
That's a job which I couldn't get wrong!"

Now, all of the children of Glasgow
Sing, *"Hector's the haggis for me!"*
As he spins them around till they're dizzy.
And fills them with magic and glee.

So, next time you visit his fairground,
Young Hector will whirl you all day.
For a haggis, his life is *perfection!*
(And it came in a round-about way.)

Tiffin's CAROUSEL
GHOST
CANDY FLOSS

CREEPY PEOPLE

We creepy people *hate* the sun!
One single beam, away we run
To look for cover far from sight,
Where we can change the day — to night!

Our dank and musty secret home
Lies underneath a brick or stone,
Where centipedes and snails can dance
With caterpillars, slugs and ants.

Crawl, slither, slather, slide.
Oh, for a place where we can hide.
A tiny corner's all we need,
Just so we can rest and feed.

Next time you lift a stone or rock
Please, don't get a frightful shock
And chase us from our favourite park!
We're friendly chaps who just love *dark*.

PROFESSOR ALBERT BOTTLEBRAIN

Professor Albert Bottlebrain
Invented crazy things:
Like teapots made of chocolate,
Or bells which never ring.

Traffic lights for hedgehogs,
Bananas with red skins,
An acid that melts *everything* —
What *did* he keep it in?

He once designed a rocket
That could fly beyond the moon,
But the silly nitwit built it
Right inside his living-room.

It smashed straight through his ceiling,
On it's way towards the stars
And took the man who lived upstairs
Way out to live on — MARS !

He invented *speeding* ointment,
And called it '*Up and Go.*'
Then poured some over Charlie Drake,
A duck who flew quite slow.

That slimy ointment on his feathers
Made poor Charlie run *amok !*
He raced five supersonic jets
Ten times around the block !

Last year that daft inventor built
A *Jurassic time- machine,*
To whiz him back into the past
And view those ancient scenes.

But Albert built it back to front,
Then took the *future* track
Way out into next century,
And can't find his way back !

JOHNNIE TROTTER

Johnnie Trotter long and fat,
The pig who thought he was a cat,
Would *meow* and clamber after birds
In a manner most absurd.
He'd sit for hours and barely stir,
Licking non-existent fur!

No milk or cream inside his sty,
He sniffed the air and wondered why,
No proper 'cat grub' ever came,
Not one small fish or slice of game.
Extremely bored with this, one day
He jumped his sty, ran fast away.

Soon John was in the farmer's house
With hopes to catch a nice fat MOUSE!
On kitchen floor, so cold and bare,
He crept along with feline care,
But stepping on a drawing pin
Caused Johnnie Trot to make a din!

The farmer's wife ran in to see
What wailing pussy this could be.
Saw Johnnie's curly tail so bold,
Emerging from a mouse's hole,
And purring with tremendous glee
As from his mouth hung rodents THREE!

"What *do* you think you're doing here?"
She bellowed loudly in his ear.
He tried to rub his fur so thick
Against her leg — it made her sick!
His sparse and scrunchy, scratchy hair
Tore both her socks from here to there.

She punched poor Johnnie Trotter's snout,
Which made him screech — and scamper out.

Then, taking refuge up a tree,
He licked his wounds, quite hurt, but free!
Though Johnnie *still* thinks he's a cat,
He now pursues, just vole — or rat!

THE GULL FROM MULL

The sailor from the Isle of Mull
Was always jolly, never dull,
With bushy whiskers wild and free,
He loved to sail far out to sea.

Whilst sailing near a distant land,
A seagull landed on his hand.
And then without a bye your leave,
It fell asleep upon his sleeve.

The sailor thought it such a cheek,
Until that gull, with open beak
Screeched and squawked in scratchy words,
"Sir, I am no common bird!

As you so kindly gave me rest
I'd like to treat you as my guest.
I am the *king* of seagulls all,
Come, fly with me. We'll have a ball!"

The sailor asked, "How can this be?
For you're not *half* as big as me.
And should you drop me from the air,
I'd hurt myself, and that's not fair!"

"Oh, don't be scared," the seagull cracked,
"My wings are MAGIC. That's a fact!"
So off they soared 'cross ocean blue,
At least ten thousand miles they flew.

At last they glided down to land,
Above a palace large and grand.
Said seagull, "Welcome to my nest."
The sailor cried, "Well I'll be blessed!"

"Dear sailor," screeched the seagull king,
"Enjoy yourself. Laugh, dance, and sing!
For soon, great feasting will begin,
While dancing doves play violins.

I've lots of special treats laid on,
Sweet nightingales will sing love songs.
My penguin waiters (so refined)
Will pour for you my finest wines."

But very soon, in fact next day,
The sailor had a price to pay.
Because he'd lived the life of kings,
All at once he grew GREY WINGS!

Then yellow beak, and feathered tail.
"Oh no!" he wailed. "No more I'll sail!"
The seagull grinned, "Oh don't be daft.
Just FLY instead." Then screeched and laughed.

At first the sailor stood quite shocked,
As on those skinny legs he rocked,
Then flapped his mighty wings *full boost*
And flew straight home to Mull — to roost!

Now every day that sailor's fed
By tourists, throwing lumps of bread.
They come in droves to visit Mull
To meet the famous BEARDED GULL!

SWEET DREAMS

If ice-cream cones were telephones,
Now, wouldn't that be cool?
Licking, as I talked to friends,
Hang up, when I was full!

If candy bars were motor cars,
I'd ride around all day,
Munching chunks of steering wheel
Have brakes — along the way!

If shoes and socks were chocolate drops
I'd walk, and run for miles,
Sometimes I'd stop to chew my socks,
Now *that* would raise some smiles!